DINOSAUR TRAIN™

Jim Henson's

A Surprise for Mum

One sunny day, Tiny, Shiny, Don and Buddy were playing Follow the Leader.

Everyone was copying Tiny, twirling and whirling around.

"Watch out, **Buddy!**" Tiny shouted. "Don't squash Mum's flowers!"

"That reminds me," Buddy replied, "you wanted to find Mum some **flowers** today."

"Yeah, today is Mum's **birthday,**" said Tiny.

"We need to get her a special present."

"What a **great** idea, Tiny! Why don't we go to the Big Pond?" said Mr. Pteranodon.

Just then, Mrs. Pteranodon flew back to the nest.

"Guess what,
Mum!"
said Tiny.

"Dad's taking us to the
Big Pond. You get the
day off!"

"A day off!" squawked Mrs. Pteranodon.

"That sounds so relaxing. I'm going to take a nap on a warm rock.

Have fun, kids!"

Mr. Pteranodon took the children and flew off to the Dinosaur Train.

"Greetings, Pteranodon family. Where are you off to today?" asked Mr. Conductor.

Don and Shiny held up their tickets.

"We're going to the **Big Pond**," said Shiny.
"We're going to find a **special** present for our mum," said Tiny.

"What a great idea!"
said Mr. Conductor.

"I'm sure you'll find what you're looking for. Next stop, Big Pond!"

Mr. Pteranodon and the kids got off the train and walked up to the Big Pond. "Look, Buddy," said Tiny.

"Flowers.

I bet Mum would like some **big** red ones!"

"**Ooh, shells,**" said Shiny.

"I'll make Mum a crown out of the shiniest ones I can find. And one for me too!"

Don flew up
to a ledge.

"I'm going to
catch the
biggest
fish in
this pond!"

"I'll help you, Don. I can be your spotter," said Mr. Pteranodon.

"Let's catch some **fish!**"

"Look, Dad. A big splash!" said Don.
"You know what that means,"
said Mr. Pteranodon. **"A big fish!"**

Don and Mr. Pteranodon dived into the water to catch
the big fish. But all they caught was a very small one!

While Mr. Pteranodon dropped the fish on the shore, Don dived back into the water.

Suddenly, Mr. Pteranodon
heard a squawk.

He looked up and
saw Don carrying
a huge fish.

"Great work!"
he shouted.

In the woods,
Buddy and Tiny
saw a bee.

"Buddy,"
said Tiny,
"bees love
flowers. Let's
follow him!"

The bee flew off
into a patch of
pink flowers.

"These are nice,"
said Buddy,
"but they aren't quite
right. Come on, bee,
help us find some
big **red** flowers
for Mum!"

Buddy and Tiny chased after the bee. It led them right to a field of big red flowers!

"These are perfect," said Tiny. "Let's go show everyone else!"

Buddy and Tiny picked up a little log that some of the red flowers were growing on, so they didn't have to pick them.

They **raced** back to the Big Pond. Everyone was waiting for them.

"Come on, Team Pteranodon," said Mr. Pteranodon.

"Let's get these presents back to the Dinosaur Train!"

That night, back at the nest,
the children gave Mrs. Pteranodon
her gifts.

"I made you a crown of the **shiniest** shells," said Shiny.

"I got you a big fish!" said Don.

"**And we found some big red flowers for your garden!**" shouted Buddy and Tiny.

"**Wow!**

These are such thoughtful presents," said Mrs. Pteranodon.

"**I'm the luckiest mum in the world!**"